P9-CRO-572

Canadian Folk Songs for the Young

Selected by Barbara Cass-Beggs

Douglas & McIntyre
Vancouver

To Duncan and Nicolas

Copyright©Barbara Cass-Beggs, 1975

All rights reserved. No part of this book may be reproduced or
transmitted in any form by any means without permission in writing
from the publisher, except by a reviewer, who may quote brief
passages in a review.

First paperback edition, 1980

Douglas & McIntyre Ltd.
1615 Venables Street
Vancouver, British Columbia

Illustrations by John Robertson
Designed by Jim Rimmer

Canadian Cataloguing in Publication Data

Main entry under title:

Canadian folk songs for the young

   Words and unacc. melodies, most of which
have chord symbols.
   Songs in languages other than English are
accompanied by English translations.
   ISBN 0-88894-065-3 bd.
   ISBN 0-88894-266-4 pa.

   1. Children's songs, Canadian.   2. Folk-songs,
Canadian.   I. Cass-Beggs, Barbara, 1904-
M1678.C35 1980   784-6'24'06   C76-161-8

CONTENTS

INTRODUCTION

Those of us who work with children realize what an important part music can play in their lives, and how essential it is to provide them with songs which are both enjoyable and musically significant.

Folk songs merit this description, and in the wide range of available folk songs there are many which appeal to children. Some can be enjoyed by the very young child along with the standard singing games and nursery rhymes–which are, of course, folk songs too.

To define a folk song is a difficult thing to do, because everyone seems to have his own definition and all the definitions differ considerably. However, let us start off with "the authorities."

Marius Barbeau, our most outstanding Canadian folk song collector and founder of the Canadian Folk Music Society, says: "What characterizes ancient folk songs is their inveterate nomadism. Born under the stars, as it were, they at once took to the road or the sea. . . . Impelled by a fate that goes back to their oral birth and transmission, far away and long ago, they had to keep on travelling. . . . To the songs, all of Europe was one country, which they criss-crossed in all directions. Often they embarked on ships and sailed the seas, landing at many ports even in America."[1]

Cecil Sharp, England's most renowned folk song collector and writer, has written an entire book devoted to defining what he considers to be the true characteristics of a folk song. He introduces *English Folk Song: Some Conclusions* with a very short definition which is worth quoting as a summary of his thinking: "In this book the word folk-song will be used exclusively to denote the song which has been created by the common people, in contradistinction to the song, popular or otherwise, which has been composed by the educated."[2]

Since a folk song is passed along orally and added to by many different people, it is well summed up by Vaughan Williams as "an air with variations."[3] He goes on to agree with Cecil Sharp and Marius Barbeau that although the original air of a folk tune is made up by an individual, the music has a communal evolution as well as the words.

In order to survive, folk songs had to be enjoyable and musically significant. Enjoyable because they deal with everyday happenings which interest children: boat building; fishing; dancing; making up nonsense rhymes because one is happy. Musically significant because, while conveying history and custom, these songs possess lively rhythms and simple but beautiful melodies.

Because this book is directed to Canadian children (although it is hoped that children from other countries will enjoy it too) the selected folk songs are all Canadian, for it is important for children to know their own songs first in order to discover their roots. According to American folk singer Alan Lomax, "The first function of music, especially folk music, is to produce a feeling of security for the listener by voicing the particular quality of a land and the life of its people. . . . Folk song calls the native back to his roots and prepares him emotionally to dance, worship, work, fight, or make love in ways normal to his place." [4]

With so many folk song books already available it may well be asked, "Why one more?" The fact is that the songs which children can enjoy most are scattered in many books, and unless one has a fairly wide knowledge of children and folk songs it is not easy to select them. And such a selection needs editing—not to censor, but to ensure that the children can understand what they sing.

Collectors preserve our songs by recording them in books and storing them in archives, but unless they are sung, songs do not truly live, and our children will not be aware of their Canadian heritage. Canadian children must be given the opportunity of acquiring a taste for their forefathers' songs. They can then move on to absorb and enjoy the remarkable variety and beauty of folk songs from other parts of the world.

Folk song on this continent is, in Alan Lomax's words, a museum of musical antiques from many lands. Canada's original folk songs were of course Indian and Eskimo, but we have inherited songs from our founding cultures—the French and British—and from the many other cultural groups which go to form the Canadian mosaic. In addition, a certain number of songs are indigenous; examples are "I'se the B'y" and "Flunky Jim."

Having taught our songs to a succession of school children, I have only included in this book those songs which they have obviously enjoyed and wanted to sing again.

Because it is interesting to know the background of the songs, there are brief notes on them which it is hoped will be read or interpreted to the children.

In general, folk songs are better unaccompanied, except perhaps for handclaps or drum beat. However, in some instances it is fun to use a guitar or autoharp, so some simple chording has been included.

The book is divided into three sections, and although children may want to sing songs from all three sections, Section One is particularly suitable for the pre-school and kindergarten level, Section Two to the younger grades and Section Three to older children. Complete notes accompany the songs in sections Two and Three, but the notes in Section One have been supplemented with introductory suggestions for the use of the songs.

My thanks go to all those who have collected these songs. I am particularly indebted to Edith Fowke, whose scholarly notes have provided the historical background material for much of my text. And thanks to Kristine and Liza Palin for helping me to choose these songs.

Sources:

[1] Marius Barbeau, *Folk Songs of Old Quebec*, National Museum of Canada.

[2] Cecil Sharp, *English Folk Song: Some Conclusions*, Methuen and Company Ltd., London, England.

[3] R. Vaughan Williams, *National Music and Other Essays*, Oxford University Press, Oxford, England.

[4] Alan Lomax, *The Folk Songs of North America*, Doubleday and Company, Inc., New York, U.S.A.

ACKNOWLEDGEMENTS

Acadian Lullaby and **Kangaroo, The:** with kind permission of the collector, Helen Creighton.

Bonhomm' Bonhomm': Allan Mills, *Chantons un peu,* Berandol Music Ltd., Scarborough, Ontario. With kind permission from Alan Mills.

Donkey Riding: collected by Thomas Wood, *Oxford Song Book 2,* Oxford University Press, Oxford, England.

Eskimo Lullaby: collected by D. H. Whitbread; published by Edith Fowke and Richard Johnston, *More Folk Songs of Canada.* With kind permission from Waterloo Music Co. Ltd., Waterloo, Ontario.

Flunky Jim, Sioux Lullaby, and **Song of Louis Riel:** collected by Barbara Cass-Beggs, *Folk Songs of Saskatchewan,* Folkways Ethnic Library F W 4312, New York, U.S.A.

Haul on the Bowline: Elizabeth B. Greenleaf and Grace Y. Mansfield, *Ballads and Sea Songs of Newfoundland,* Harvard University Press, Cambridge, U.S.A.

Icelandic Lullaby: collected by Horpuhl Jomar, *Islenz Songlog.* First published by Fjorar Karlmannar and Sigfus Einarsson, Reykjavik, 1905. From Department of Icelandic Literature, University of Manitoba, Winnipeg, Manitoba.

Iroquois Lullaby: Edith Fowke, Helmut Blume, Alan Mills, *Canada's Story in Song,* W. J. Gage Ltd. Reprinted by permission of Gage Educational Publishing Ltd., Agincourt, Ontario.

I'se the B'y that Builds the Boat, Lots of Fish in Bonavist' Harbour, and **Paper of Pins, A:** collected by Kenneth Peacock, Information Canada, Ottawa, Ontario. With kind permission of the collector and Information Canada.

Jack Was Every Inch a Sailor: *Old Time Songs and Poetry of Newfoundland,* Gerald S. Doyle Ltd., St. John's, Newfoundland, with kind permission.

Klondike and **The Sailor's Alphabet:** sung by Captain Charles Cates. **Way Up the Ucletaw:** sung by Ed Dalby. From the Phil Thomas collection, Vancouver, British Columbia. With kind permission of the collector.

La Poulette grise: Alan Mills, *Favourite French Folk Songs,* Embassy Music Corp., New York, U.S.A.

Rattle on the Stovepipe: collected by Edith Fowke; published by Edith Fowke and Richard Johnston, *More Folk Songs of Canada.* With kind permission from Waterloo Music Ltd., Waterloo, Ontario.

She's Like the Swallow: Maud Karpeles, *Folk Songs of Newfoundland,* reprinted by permission of Faber and Faber Ltd., London, England.

Song of the Rabbit and **Song of the Seagull:** collected by Beverly Cavanagh. With kind permission of the collector.

Zing, Zing, Zing: collected by S. J. Germain Lemieux, *Chansonnier franco-ontarien 1*, La Société historique du Nouvel-Ontario, Sudbury, Ontario. With kind permission of the collector.

The main reference for the following songs is Ernest Gagnon's *Chansons populaires du Canada*, Editions Beauchemin, Montreal, Québec, 1865:

Ah! Si mon moine voulait danser!
Dans tous les cantons
D'où viens-tu, bergère?
En roulant ma boule
Gai lon la, gai le rosier
Huron Carol, The
Un Canadien errant
Vive la Canadienne

TRANSLATIONS

Acadian Lullaby: Barbara Cass-Beggs.
Ah! Si mon moine voulait danser!: Edith Fowke
Gai lon la, gai le rosier: verse one by Edith Fowke; new verses by Barbara Cass-Beggs.
Iroquois Lullaby: English by Alan Mills; French by Evy Paraskevopoulos
La Poulette grise: Alan Mills
Bonhomm', Bonhomm': Alan Mills
Icelandic Lullaby: Barbara Cass-Beggs
J'entends le moulin: Edith Fowke
D'où viens-tu, bergère?: based on Murray Gibbon's. Verse one by Edith Fowke; verses two and three by Barbara Cass-Beggs
Huron Carol: English by J.E. Middleton, used by permission of the Frederick Harris Music Company, Oakville, Ontario.
Sioux Lullaby: Barbara Cass-Beggs
Song of Louis Riel: Barbara Cass-Beggs
Song of the Rabbit and **Song of the Seagull:** Beverly Cavanagh
Words for **The Top, The Merry-Go-Round, Our Toboggan** and **See the Leaves** by Barbara Cass-Beggs.

SECTION 1

ACADIAN LULLABY

With its pentatonic (5 note) pattern, **Acadian Lullaby** is easily sung to solfa, or played on a xylophone, chime bars, or the black notes of the piano. It is also very easily accompanied with other notes or combination of notes from the pentatonic scale.

AH! SI MON MOINE VOULAIT DANSER!

When the children sing **The Top** version of this song, they can pretend to whip tops. Similarly, when they sing **The Merry-Go-Round** they can move in a circle, pretending to be on horses on a merry-go-round. They can sing the song as they go around the first time; then the music can quicken up while they go around again, gradually slowing up as the merry-go-round comes to a halt.

ALOUETTE

This is an obvious solo (teacher) and chorus (children) song with appropriate actions.

EN ROULANT MA BOULE

En Roulant is a good practice song for the French "en" sound. The children enjoy throwing an imaginary or real ball to this little chorus.

See the Leaves are Falling Down lends itself to actions. It is fun to use real leaves and have the children listen to the sound that they make.

BEHIND MY AUNTIE'S COTTAGE

After the whole song has been sung once, each verse can be used for movement, verse one "wandering in the wood and listening to the birds," verse two "skating" and verse three "swimming." Part of the class can sing while the others move, or the song can be played on the piano or autoharp.

IROQUOIS LULLABY

Although lullabies should be unaccompanied (can you imagine a mother playing an instrument while she lulls her baby?) a slow drum beat goes well with this Indian lullaby. If the group sings the Iroquois, English and French versions in succession, three children can have a turn on the drum.

OUR TOBOGGAN

This song can be learned unaccompanied by action, and when the children know it they can dramatize it. Please note the built-in discipline of "stop, stop, stop" *before* they tumble onto the ground! Most easily played outside, this song needs lots of space.

ACADIAN LULLABY

Dors, dors, le p'tit bi-bi. C'est le beau p'tit bi-bi à ma-ma.
Sleep, sleep lit-tle ba - by. You're such a love-ly mo-ther's lit- tle one.

Dors, dors, dors, dors, Dors, dors le bi- bi à ma-ma. De-
Sleep, sleep, sleep, sleep, Sleep, sleep mo-ther's ba — by. To -

main s'y fait beau j'irons au grand-père. Dors, dors le p'tit bi- bi.
mor-row if it's fine we will see grand-pa. Sleep, sleep, lit-tle ba - by.

Dors, dors, dors, dors, dors, le beau p'tit bi-bi à ma-ma.
Sleep, sleep, sleep, sleep, sleep, love-ly one, mo-ther's lit-tle ba — by.

Dors, dors, le p'tit bibi.
C'est le beau p'tit bibi à mama.
Dors, dors, dors, dors,
Dors, dors, le bibi à mama.
Demain s'y fait beau j'irons au
    grand-père.
Dors, dors, le p'tit bibi.
Dors, dors, dors, dors,
Dors, le beau p'tit bibi à mama.

Sleep, sleep, little baby.
You're such a lovely Mother's little
    one.
Sleep, sleep, sleep, sleep,
Sleep, sleep, Mother's baby.
Tomorrow if it's fine we will see
    Grandpa.
Sleep, sleep, little baby.
Sleep, sleep, sleep, sleep,
Sleep, lovely one, Mother's little baby.

ACADIAN LULLABY
*This very beautiful lullaby comes from the
Maritime provinces. It was sung to Helen
Creighton by a woman who lives in the village
of Pubuico. The song goes back to the time
of the French who settled in these parts
and who were called Acadians. It is based on
a 5-note (pentatonic) scale.*

AH! SI MON MOINE VOULAIT DANSER

Ah! si mon moine vou — lait dan-ser, Ah! si mon moine vou —
Oh! if my top will— dance with me, Oh! if my top will—

lait dan-ser, Un-ca-pu-chon je lui don-ne-rais, Un
dance with me, So ve-ry hap-py—— I shall be, So

ca-pu-chon je lui don-ne-rais. Dan-se, mon moine, dan-se. Tu
ve-ry hap-py I shall be. Dance,my top, come dance now; —

n'en-tends pas la dan-se. Tu n'en-tends pas mon mou-
Spin a-round, a-round, now. I love my top to ——

lin lon là! Tu n'en-tends pas mon mou-lin mar-cher.
dance with me; He spins a-round so—— mer-ri-ly.

Ah! si mon moine voulait danser,
Ah! si mon moine voulait danser,
Un capuchon je lui donnerais,
Un capuchon je lui donnerais.
Danse, mon moine, danse.
Tu n'entends pas la danse.
Tu n'entends pas mon moulin lon là!
Tu n'entends pas mon moulin marcher.

The Top
Oh! if my top will dance with me,
Oh! if my top will dance with me,
So very happy I shall be,
So very happy I shall be.
Dance, my top, come dance now;
Spin around around now.
I love my top to dance with me;
He spins around so merrily.

Ah! if my monk will dance,
Ah! if my monk will dance,
I will give him a hood (cowl),
I will give him a hood.
Dance, my monk, dance.
You don't { know how to dance. / hear the dance
You don't hear my mill
You don't hear how my mill turns on.

The Merry-Go-Round
Oh! off we go on the merry-go-round,
Oh! off we go on the merry-go-round.
Our feet can scarcely touch the ground
As we go whirling round and round.
Gee up, horsie, whoa there!
We love to ride on the merry-go-round.
It's quite the nicest thing in town.

AH! SI MON MOINE VOULAIT DANSER

This happy dance tune, which originally described all the things a young lady would give a monk ("moine") if only he would dance, was sung by the French voyageurs and the early habitants in New France. The French words seem to suggest that the monk's inattention to the sound of the mill wheel is part of his inability or unwillingness to dance— that is, he lacks a sense of rhythm. (Of course, this may be reading a fairly subtle idea into the words.)

Because "moine" can mean "top" as well as "monk", the children soon began to sing this tune as they whipped their tops. Here are some top-whipping words as well as the original French words. It is such an infectious tune that the children may want to sing it often to various sets of words, including those about a merry-go-round.

ALOUETTE!

O alouette, gentille alouette,
Alouette, je t'y plumerai.
Alouette, gentille alouette,
Alouette, je t'y plumerai.
1. Je t'y plumerai la têt',
   Je t'y plumerai la têt'.
   Et la têt', et la têt',
   Alouett
   Alouett.

2. Je t'y plumerai le bec
3. Je t'y plumerai le nez
4. Je t'y plumerai les yeux
5. Je t'y plumerai le cou
6. Je t'y plumerai le dos
7. Je t'y plumerai les patt's.

(Je t'y plumerai: I will pluck your . . .)
têt(e): head
bec: beak
nez: nose
yeux: eyes
cou: neck
dos: back
pattes: feet

ALOUETTE!

*Like other cumulative fun songs, Alouette has
a phrase added to the verse each time you
sing it. The chorus echoes the solo singer.
There are a number of verses and you can
add more, as long as the soloist can remember
them.*

EN ROULANT MA BOULE

En rou - lant ma boule — rou - lant, En rou-lant ma bou - !e.
On, roll on, my ball, — roll on; On, roll on, my ball, roll on.

En roulant ma boule roulant,
En roulant ma boule.

On, roll on, my ball, roll on;
On, roll on, my ball.

See the Leaves
See, the leaves are falling down,
Red and yellow, gold and brown.
See them twist and turn around
As they flutter to the ground.
Let us sweep them into a pile,
Rustling, rustling, all the while.
As they lie upon the ground
Still they make a rustling sound.

EN ROULANT MA BOULE
*The early explorers sang while they paddled
Canada's rivers, in order to keep together and
to stay alert on their long canoe voyages.
They therefore needed songs with a great
many verses, and ones that had a verse and
a chorus, so that those who did not know the
verse could at least join in to sing the chorus.
The men singing this song were French
explorers, or coureurs-de-bois, who adopted an
old fifteenth century French song with a
catchy tune, probably changing or adding to
the words as they felt inclined.*

*Here is the chorus of this song. As it has such
a catchy tune for doing things to, it could also
be sung as a leaf-raking autumn song. You
could make up additional words which would
suit snow-shovelling or some other activity.*

GAI LON LA, GAI LE ROSIER

Par derrièr' chez ma tante
Lui y-a-t-un bois joli.
Le rossignol y chante
Et le jour et la nuit.
Gai lon la, gai le rosier
Du joli mois de mai.

Behind My Auntie's Cottage
Behind my Auntie's cottage
There is a forest gay.
Nightingales there are singing
All through the night and day.
Gay lon la, gay is the rose
This lovely month of May.

Behind my Auntie's cottage
There is a lovely lake
Where we can swim in summer
And pleasant picnics take.
Swim, swim, swim, oh it is fun
When we can go and swim.

Behind my Auntie's cottage
There is a lovely lake,
And when the water's frozen
We can all go and skate.
Skate, skate, skate, oh it is fun
When we can go and skate.

GAI LON LA, GAI LE ROSIER
*This French song has become well known in
Canada because of its charming melody. It
describes a visit to an aunt in the country.
In the first verse we have the original French
words, which mention a bird that does not
exist in Canada. (You might be able to listen
to a record of the nightingale's beautiful song.)
In place of the many remaining verses, which
tell what an adult would do at this cottage in
France, here are two other verses describing
what a Canadian child would do if visiting
an aunt in her Canadian cottage.*

IROQUOIS LULLABY

Ho ho — wa-ta-nay, Ho ho — wa-ta-nay
Sleep, sleep, — lit-tle one, Sleep, sleep, — lit-tle one,
Do, do, — mon pe-tit, Do, do, — mon pe-tit,

Ho, ho — wa-ta-nay, Ki - yo-ke-na, Ki - yo-ke - na.
Sleep, sleep, — lit-tle one, O, go to sleep, O go to sleep.
Do, do — mon pe-tit, Et bonne nu-it, Et bonne nu-it.

Ho ho wa-ta-nay
Ho ho wa-ta-nay
Ho ho wa ta-nay
Ki yo ke na
Ki yo ke na.

Sleep, sleep, little one,
Sleep, sleep, little one,
Sleep, sleep, little one,
O, go to sleep.
O, go to sleep.

Do, do, mon petit,
Do, do, mon petit,
Do, do, mon petit,
Et bonne nuit,
Et bonne nuit.

IROQUOIS LULLABY
This lullaby can be sung in Iroquois, English or French. Alan Mills, who has collected and sung many Canadian folk songs, was the first to write it down. It was sung to him by the Iroquois of Caughnawaga, which is on the south side of the St. Lawrence about ten miles west of Montreal. Try to accompany it with a very soft drum beat.

OUR TOBOGGAN

French Folk Melody **DANS TOUS LES CANTONS.**

Come, let us pull, pull, pull
Our toboggan up the hill.
Come, let us pull, pull, pull
Our toboggan up the hill.
Now we are at the top
And sliding swiftly down,
And sliding swiftly down,
And sliding swiftly down
Until we stop, stop, stop!
And tumble in the snow.

OUR TOBOGGAN

The opening verses of the French words that go with this melody describe the fun that boys and girls have together when they are young, but later verses paint a very gloomy picture of what happens to them when they grow up and get married. Because the gloomy words do not seem to fit this lively melody, the song is not often sung. New words can be sung to the tune, which obviously suits some kind of open air activity such as tobogganning. You can probably think of still other activities to sing about, and make up your own words to fit this melody.

LA POULETTE GRISE

C'est la pou-let-te gri-se Qui pond dans l'é-
There is a grey hen, ba-by, In the church, my

gli-se. Ell' va pon-dre un pet-tit co-co Pour son p'tit qui va
ba-by. She will lay a pret-ty lit-le egg Just for you if you'll

fair' do-di-che. Ell' va pon-dre un pet-tit co-co
go to sleep. ―― She will lay a pret-ty lit-tle egg

Pour son p'tit qui va fair' do do. Do-di-che, do-do.
Just for you if you'll go to sleep. Sleep now, my ba-by.

C'est la poulette grise
Qui pond dans l'église.
Ell' va pondre un petit coco
Pour son p'tit qui va fair' dodiche;
Ell' va pondre un petit coco
Pour son p'tit qui va fair' dodo.
Dodiche, dodo.
C'est la poulette brune
Qui pond dans la lune.
C'est la poulette blanche
Qui pond dans les branches.

There is a grey hen, baby,
In the church, my baby.
She will lay a pretty little egg
Just for you if you go to sleep now;
She will lay a pretty little egg
Just for you if you go to sleep now.
Sleep now, my baby.

There is a brown hen, baby,
In the town, my baby.

There is a white hen, baby
In the light, my baby.

LA POULETTE GRISE

This is a French Canadian lullaby (probably originally French) about hens of different colours. Only a few of Alan Mills's suggested verses are here; the singers may have the fun of making up additional ones. The trick, of course, is to match the colour word with a rhyming word.

Alan has changed the style of the verse in the English version so that rhymes may fit in more easily. As it is a lullaby and babies sometimes take a long while to go to sleep, any number of verses may be added.

SECTION 2

BLOOD ON THE SADDLE

There was blood on the sad-dle, and blood all a-round, And a great big pud-dle of blood on the ground

1. There was blood on the saddle
   And blood all around,
   And a great big puddle
   Of blood on the ground.

2. The cowboy lay in it
   All covered with gore,
   And he won't go riding
   No broncos no more.

3. O pity the cowboy
   All bloody and red,
   For his bronco fell on him
   And mashed in his head.

BLOOD ON THE SADDLE

Here is a very bloody cowboys' song which describes a rodeo accident. The scene described is rather gruesome, but the song seems to have been sung with great gusto and quite a lot of enjoyment, as if the tale were never intended to be taken too seriously.

Although this song may have come originally from Arizona, a Dr. E. A. Corbett remembers hearing it sung in Calgary as early as 1905.

BONHOMM', BONHOMM'

Bon - homm', Bon - homm' sais - tu jou — er? Bon - homm', Bon -
Good friend, good friend, say, can you play? Good friend, good

homm', sais - tu jou — er? Sais - tu jou — er de ce vio - lon -
friend, say can you play? Say, can you play — the vi - o -

là? Sais - tu jou - er de ce vio - lon - là? —— Zing, zing,
lin? Say, can you play — the vi - o - lin? —— Zing, zing,

zing, de ce vio - lon - là! Zing, zing, zing, de ce vio - lon - là! —— Bon -
zing, on the vi - o - lin! Zing, zing, zing, on the vi - o - lin! —— Good

homm' Tu n'est pas maitr' dans ta mai - son Quand nous y som - mes.——
friend, You are not boss in your own house, when we come here to play.

The final Bonhomm' can also be sung with solo and chorus if wanted, i.e.

Bon - homm' Bon - homm'

22

Bonhomm', Bonhomm'

Solo: Bonhomm', Bonhomm', sais-tu jouer?
Chorus: Bonhomm', Bonhomm', sais-tu jouer?
Solo: Sais-tu jouer de ce violon-là?
Chorus: Sais-tu jouer de ce violon-là?
Solo: Zing, zing, zing, de ce violon-là!
Chorus: Zing, zing, zing, de ce violon-là!
Bonhomm',
Tu n'est pas maitr' dans ta maison,
Quand nous y sommes.

Second Soloist: Bonhomm', Bonhomm', sais-tu jouer?
Chorus: Bonhomm', Bonhomm', sais-tu jouer?
Second Soloist: Sais-tu jouer de ce flûte-là?
Chorus: Sais-tu jouer de ce flûte-là?
Second Soloist: Flût', flût', flût' de cett' flût' qui flûte!
Chorus: Flût', flût', flût' de cett' flût' qui flûte!
First Soloist: Zing, zing, zing de ce violon-là!
Chorus: Zing, zing, zing de ce violon-là!
Bonhomm'!
Tu n'est pas maitr' dans ta maison,
Quand nous y sommes!

Third Soloist: Bonhomm', Bonhomm', sais-tu jouer?
Chorus: Bonhomm', Bonhomm', sais-tu jouer?
Third Soloist: Sais-tu jouer de ce tambour-là?
Chorus: Sais-tu jouer de ce tambour-là?
Third Soloist: Boom, boom, boom de ce tambour-là!
Chorus: Boom, boom, boom de ce tambour-là!
Second Soloist: Flût', flût', flût' de cett' flût' qui flûte!
Chorus: Flût', flût', flût' de cett' flût' qui flûte!
First Soloist: Zing, zing, zing de ce violon-là!
Chorus: Zing, zing, zing de ce violon-là!
Bonhomm'!
Tu n'est pas maitr' dans ta maison,
Quand nous y sommes!

Good friend, good friend, say can you
   play?
Good friend, good friend, say can you
   play?
Say, can you play the violin?
Say, can you play the violin?
Zing, zing, zing, on the violin!
Zing, zing, zing, on the violin!
Good friend,
You are not boss in your own house
When we come here to play.

Good friend, good friend, say can you
   play?
Good friend, good friend, say can you
   play?
Say, can you play on the little flute?
Say, can you play on the little flute?
Floo, floo, floo on the little flute!
Floo, floo, floo on the little flute!
Zing, zing, zing, on the violin!
Zing, zing, zing, on the violin!
Good friend,
You are not boss in your own house
When we come here to play.

Good friend, good friend, say can you
   play?
Good friend, good friend, say can you
   play?
Say, can you play on the big bass drum?
Say, can you play on the big bass drum?
Boom, boom, boom, on the big bass
   drum!
Boom, boom, boom, on the big bass
   drum!
Floo, floo, floo on the little flute!
Floo, floo, floo on the little flute!
Zing, zing, zing on the violin!
Zing, zing, zing on the violin!
Good friend,
You are not boss in your own house
When we come here to play.

BONHOMM', BONHOMM'

Bonhomme *did not originate in French-speaking Canada, but is very popular there. Like the other cumulative song* **Alouette**, *it is very easy to sing in the original tongue, so try it in French even though the English words are given.*

The soloist introduces one instrument after another, mimicking its sound in the "zing, zing, zing" line and miming the action of playing it. The chorus echoes the soloist. Any number of instruments can be added or substituted for the ones mentioned here. It is a good way of getting to know the names of musical instruments in French.

DONKEY RIDING

Were you ev - er in Que - bec Stow - ing tim - ber on the deck,

Where there's a king with a gold-en crown, Rid - ing on a don - key?

Hey ho! A - way we go! Don - key rid - ing, don - key rid - ing,

Hey ho! A - way we go! Rid - ing on a don - key.

Were you ever in Quebec
Stowing timber on the deck,
Where there's a king with a golden
   crown,
Riding on a donkey?

Chorus
Hey ho! Away we go,
Donkey riding, donkey riding,
Hey ho! Away we go,
Riding on a donkey.

Were you ever in Cardiff Bay,
Where the folk all shout "Hurray!
Here come John with his three months
   pay,
Riding on a donkey."

DONKEY RIDING

This song is not about the thistle-eating, braying kind of donkey, but about the mechanical kind which powered the winch on cargo boats; this was called a "donkey engine." The song was sung by sailors to keep themselves happy and working together while they loaded up the boat. As you see, the cargo was timber (wood) from Quebec, which was taken from the port of Quebec to the port of Cardiff, Wales. (Originally these ships sailed from Glasgow and Liverpool, ports in Scotland and England.) Because the men thought that they were well paid, they sang about "a king with a golden crown." The cargo boats travelled very slowly, so the sailors came home with "three months pay," which must have seemed quite a lot of money.

In order to sing this song as the sailors did, it is important to keep the time and the rhythm very exact. Donkey Riding sounds excellent if arranged for percussion instruments.

ESKIMO LULLABY

Still now and hear my sing - ing; Sleep through the night, my dar - ling. We have a ti - ny daugh - ter, Thanks be to God who sent her.

Still now and hear my singing,
Sleep through the night, my darling,
We have a tiny daughter,
Thanks be to God who sent her.

Though she as yet knows nothing,
She is so sweet I'm singing.
We have a tiny daughter,
Thanks be to God who sent her.

ESKIMO LULLABY
This a lullaby which was sung by an Eskimo family in Cape Dorset on the southern coast of Baffinland. It is quite slow and needs lots of breath, so sit up tall and take a deep breath before trying to sing it. In the first bar you will notice the syncopated beat. Perhaps this lullaby would be easier to sing rhythmically if it were accompanied with a drum beat, which could be practised before you sing the song.

FLUNKY JIM

I am the flun-ky of the house, They call me Flun-ky Jim. — You'll find me knock-ing a - round the yard in a hat with-out a brim. — My o - ver-alls are shab - by and I have no shirt at all —— But I'm go - ing to get a new out -fit with my goph -er tail next fall. — Knock-ing a - round the yard, boys, knock-ing a - round the yard. — It is -n't an - y ea - sy job, don't fool your-self, old pard. — My o - ver-alls are shab - by and I have no shirt at all. —— But I'm go - ing to get a new out - fit with my go - pher tails next fall. —

I am the flunky of the house,
They call me flunky Jim.
You'll find me knocking around the
  yard
In a hat without a brim.
My overalls are shabby,
And I have no shirt at all
But I'm going to get a new outfit
With my gopher tails next fall.

Chorus

Knocking around the yard, boys,
Knocking around the yard,
It isn't an easy job,
Don't fool yourself, old pard.
My overalls are shabby,
And I have no shirt at all
But I'm going to get a new outfit
With my gopher tails next fall.

I've counted all my gopher tails;
I've almost got enough
To buy a hat, a fancy shirt,
And pants that have a cuff.
And then I'll hand my old ones on;
They really are too small.
Oh, I'll be swell, when once I sell
My gopher tails next fall.

FLUNKY JIM

This song was sung to me in Saskatoon, Saskatchewan, by the grandson of the man— a teacher— who made it up. In the years known as the "Depression", when many people were out of work and money was very scarce, the children were given money by the government for every gopher tail that they turned in. (Gophers ate the already scarce grain crops.) Jim was the youngest boy in this family and his father made up this song after listening to Jim bragging about the new clothes he was going to get with his gopher money. Like **I'se the B'y,** *this is a skipping tune.*

ICELANDIC LULLABY

Bi bi og bla-ka
(Bye, bye and hush now)
Can you see the swans fly? You
may pre-tend to go to sleep, but
I know you will want to peep.
Bi-um bi-um bam-ba
(Lul-la-by my ba-by,)
Sleep, my lit-tle ba-by. You'll
fall a-sleep when your thoughts stray to
lit-tle lambs at play. —

Bibi og blaka,
Can you see the swans fly?
You may pretend to go to sleep
But I know you will want to peep.
Bium bium bamba, sleep, my little
     baby.
You'll fall asleep when your thoughts
     stray
To little lambs at play.

ICELANDIC LULLABY

*As you probably know, there are many
Icelandic Canadians; most live in Manitoba
and Saskatchewan. As most Icelandic families
still speak Icelandic, this very lovely and
well-known lullaby is still sung by them.*

*Most lullabies tell the baby to go to sleep, but
this one suggests that the baby stay awake—
at least long enough to see the swans fly, for*

*according to an old Icelandic legend, when
the swans fly they also sing with a sound like
silver bells. Thus encouraged, Baby tries to stay
awake, but the effort is too great and he
promptly falls asleep, which is probably what
Mother wanted all along!*

*Thinking of "little lambs at play" might be a
baby's version of "counting sheep" in order
to fall asleep.*

I'SE THE B'Y THAT BUILDS THE BOAT

I'se the b'y that builds — the boat, And I'se the b'y that sails her.

I'se the b'y that catch-es the fish And takes 'em home to Li- zer.

Hip yer part- ner, Sal- ly Tibbo! Hip yer part- ner, Sal- ly Brown.

Fo- go, Twil- lin- gate, Mor'-ton's Har- bour, All a- round the cir- cle.

I'se the b'y that builds the boat
And I'se the b'y that sails her,
I'se the b'y that catches the fish
And takes them home to Lizer.

Chorus
Hip yer partner,
Sally Tibbo!
Hip yer partner,
Sally Brown.
Fogo, Twillingate, Mor'ton's Harbour,
All around the circle.

I don't want your maggoty fish
That's no good for winter;
I can buy as good as that
Down in Bonavista.

I'SE THE B'Y THAT BUILDS THE BOAT
This song comes from Newfoundland and was made up by the men who built and sailed the fishing boats. It is a song to dance to and has a number of verses. Of these I have included only two, because the singers can make up some of their own, if any more are wanted. The three place-names (Fogo, Twillingate and Mor'ton's Harbour) are little ports, around Notre Dame Bay in northwestern Newfoundland. You will notice that the sailors say "b'y" instead of "boy." You will also notice if you clap the rhythm of this song that it is a skipping tune.

JACK WAS EVERY INCH A SAILOR

1. Now 'twas twenty-five or thirty years
   since Jack first saw the light.
   He came into this world of woe one
   dark and stormy night.
   He was born on board his father's
   ship as she was lying to
   'Bout twenty-five or thirty miles
   southeast of Bacalhao.

2. When Jack grew up to be a man,
   he went to Labrador;
   He fished in Indian Harbour, where
   his father fished before.
   On his returning in the fog, he met a
   heavy gale,
   And Jack was swept into the sea and
   swallowed by a whale.

Refrain

Jack was every inch a sailor,
Five and twenty years a whaler;
Jack was every inch a sailor,
He was born upon the bright blue
sea.

3. The whale went straight for Baffin's
    Bay 'bout ninety knots an hour,
    And ev'ry time he'd blow a spray
    he'd send it in a shower.
    "Oh now," says Jack unto himself,
    "I must see what he's about";
    He caught the whale all by the tail
    and turned him inside out.

JACK WAS EVERY INCH A SAILOR

Jack provides us with a humorous version of "Jonah and the whale." This popular song has been sung in Newfoundland for over fifty years.

Bacalhao (pronounced Back-a-loo) is a rocky island off the east coast of Newfoundland where there is an important lighthouse. Indian Harbour, on the Labrador coast, was a well known cod-fishing centre around the turn of the century.

This song is well travelled and better known than most of the songs in this book. Because of its lively words but somewhat monotonous tune it needs to be sung briskly and not allowed to drag.

J'ENTENDS LE MOULIN

J'entends le moulin, tique tique taque,
J'entends le moulin taqué.
Mon père a fait bâtir maison
J'entends le moulin taqué.
L'a fait bâtir à trois pignons
Tique taque, tique taque,
J'entends le moulin tique tique taque,
J'entends le moulin taqué.

I hear the mill wheel ticker ticker tacker,
I hear the mill wheel turning.
My father builds himself a house.
I hear the mill wheel turning.
He has three carpenters to help.
Ticker tacker, ticker tacker,
I hear the mill wheel ticker ticker tacker,
I hear the mill wheel turning.

J'ENTENDS LE MOULIN

This French song, which has been adopted by Canadians, is really two songs: the verse is one; the chorus, another. Whatever its origin, it is fun to sing, particularly in French. One can almost hear the mill wheel turning, especially if rhythm sticks or tone blocks are used for the "tique taque" part.

THE KANGAROO

A kangaroo sat on an oak
To my inkum-kiddy-kum-ki-mo,
Watching a tailor mend his coat
To my inkum-kiddy-kum-ki-mo.

Ki-mi-nee-ro, kiddy-kum-kee-o
Ki-mi-nee-ro, ki-mo.
Ba ba ba ba, billy illy inkum,
In-kum, kiddy-kum, ki-mo.

THE KANGAROO

Most of us have tried the "whispering game," in which a player whispers a written message quickly to someone who in turn whispers what he has heard to someone else, and by the time it has been whispered to about ten people it often sounds nothing like the original message. Something like this has happened to **The Kangaroo,** *which is a very old song dating back to the sixteenth century. In the original, the "kangaroo" was a crow, which of course sounds more sensible.*

The other words of the verses are fairly accurate, but many nonsense words were needed to fill out the rest of the melody. Helen Creighton, who collected this song in Nova Scotia, must have had a difficult time deciding how to write them all out. The tune is tricky, so you may find that it takes practice to say all these nonsense sounds quickly and clearly.

SECTION 3

D'OU VIENS-TU, BERGERE?

D' où viens - tu, ber-gè -re, D' où viens - tu ?

D'où viens - tu, ber-gè - re, D' où viens - tu ?

Je viens de l'é - ta - ble ———— De m'y pro - me - ner.

J'ai vu un mi - ra - cle ce soir ar - ri - vé.

2. Qu'as-tu vu, bergère, } repeat
Qu'as-tu vu?
"J'ai vu dans la crèche
Un petit enfant
Sur la paille fraîche
Mis bien tendrement."

3. Est-il beau, bergère, } repeat
Est-il beau?
"Plus beau que la lune,
Aussi le soleil.
Jamais dans le monde
On vit son pareil."

Whence come you, shepherd maiden,?

1. Whence, O shepherd maiden, } repeat
Whence come you?
"I come from the stable
Where this very night
Mine eyes have been dazzled
By a wond'rous sight."

2. What saw you, O maiden, } repeat
What saw you?
"There within the manger
A little child I saw,
Sweetly he lay sleeping
On the fresh-piled straw."

3. Was he fair, O maiden, } repeat
Was he fair?
"Fairer than the moon is;
Fairer than the sun.
Never in the world was
Such a lovely one."

D'OU VIENS-TU, BERGERE?

This carol came from France but is sung everywhere in Canada and is regarded as French Canadian. It has a question and answer form which makes it very easy to learn. As you are likely to sing the Huron carol in translation, this carol ought to be sung in French.

HAUL ON THE BOWLINE

Haul on the bow - line so ear - ly in the morn - ing,

Haul on the bow - line, the bow - line haul!

2. Haul on the bowline,
   Kitty is me darling.
   Haul on the bowline,
   The bowline *haul*.

3. Haul on the bowline,
   Our bully ship's a-rolling.
   Haul on the bowline,
   The bowline *haul*.

HAUL ON THE BOWLINE

Like **Donkey Riding**, *this is a sea shanty;
sailors sang it to pace their work as they
hauled on a rope together. It was originally
sung by British sailors, and was passed on by
early British explorers to Canadian seamen.
The Canadians sang it not only at sea but
also when they sailed on the Great Lakes.*

*The bowline, pronounced "bo'lin," was a very
important rope on the early square-rigged
sailing ships. It was fastened to the edge of the
sail so that men could haul on it to flatten the
sail and get the cutting edge into the wind.
Later, when the design of sailing ships was
changed, this line became less important;
however, the song was still sung when a short,
hard pull was needed.*

*To see how useful this sort of song was,
pretend that you are pulling on a rope and
giving your hardest pull on the word "haul."*

THE HURON CAROL

'Twas in the moon of win-ter time, when all the birds had fled, That migh-ty Git-chi-Man-i-tou sent an-gel choirs in-stead. Be-fore their light the stars grew dim, and wan-d'ring hunt-ers heard the hymn— Je-sus, your king is born, Je-sus is born, In ex-cel-sis glo-ri-a!

2. Within a lodge of broken bark
The tender babe was found.
A ragged robe of rabbit skin
Enwrapped his beauty round,
And as the hunter braves drew nigh
The angel song rang loud and high.
"Jesus, your king, is born,
Jesus is born,
In excelsis gloria."

Jésus est né

Chrétiens, prenez courage,
Jésus Sauveur est né.
Du malin les ouvrages
A jamais sont ruinés.
Quand il chante merveille
A ces troublants appas
Ne prêtez plus l'oreille.
"Jésus est né,
In excelsis gloria."

THE HURON CAROL

This song is really the first Canadian Christmas carol, as it was written in the Huron language to a French tune. The writer was probably Father Jean Brébeuf, a Jesuit missionary who lived and worked with the Huron Indians from 1626 to 1649. When the Hurons were attacked by the Iroquois, the survivors fled, some going to live in Lorette near Quebec City. They must have continued to sing this song,

for later it was translated into French by another Jesuit priest, Father de Villeneuve, under the title **Jésus est né.** *In 1926 a Canadian poet, J. E. Middleton, wrote the very beautiful English words, which are an interpretation rather than a literal translation. Because these words not only fit the melody very well but also seem to capture the feeling of an Indian carol, they deserve first preference for singing.*

KLONDIKE

P.J. Thomas Collection

Oh, come to the place where they struck it rich, Come where the trea-sure lies hid! Where your hat full of mud is a five-pound note And a clod on your heel is a

Chorus:

quid! __ Klon - dike! Klon - dike! Oh, lab -el your lug - gage for Klon -dike. Oh, there ain't no luck in the town to - day; There ain't no work down Mood- y - ville way. So pack up your traps and be off, I say, Off and a - way to the Klon - dike!

Chorus

Klondike! Klondike!
Label your luggage for Klondike.
Oh, there ain't no luck in the
   town today;
There ain't no work down
   Moodyville way.
So pack up your traps and be off,
   I say,
Off and away to the Klondike!

2. Oh, they scratches the earth and it
      tumbles out,
   More than your hands can hold;
   For the hills above and the plains
      beneath
   Are crackin' and bustin' with gold!

KLONDIKE

This song grew out of the gold rush excitement which started in 1896 with the discovery of gold in the Yukon, an area east of the Yukon river whose principal town was Dawson. The economic depression of the 1890s still gripped the Northwest, and the gold rush business helped to get things moving again in Seattle, Victoria and Vancouver. Moodyville was the old millsite waterfront area of the growing North Vancouver.

Klondike might well have begun its life in the music halls or bars. Or it could have started as a musical advertisement of gear for the Klondike, for in Vancouver, outfitters actually had parades of mules loaded with a miner's complete equipment and bedecked with the names of the companies selling the goods. Whatever its origin, it is a lively tune full of a probably unjustified, but contagious, optimism!

LOTS OF FISH IN BONAVIST' HARBOUR

Oh! there's
Lots of fish in Bonavist' harbour;
Lots of fish right in around here.
Boys and girls are fishing together,
Forty-five from Carbonear.

Chorus
Oh!
Catch-a-hold this one, catch-a-hold
    that one,
Swing around this one, dance around
    she,
Catch-a-hold this one, catch-a-hold
    that one,
Diddledum this one, diddledum dee.

LOTS OF FISH IN BONAVIST' HARBOUR
*Here is a Newfoundland fishing song which
points out that Carbonear, the largest town in
Conception Bay just west of St. John's,*
*provides a large number of men to help with
the fishing. It was probably sung when they had
caught a great many fish and were feeling
ready for square dancing.*

A PAPER OF PINS

Man.

1. I'll give to you a paper of pins;
   It is the way my love begins,
   If you might marry me, me, me,
   If you might marry me.

3. I'll give to you a suit of red,
   Stitched around with golden thread.
   (If you . . .)

5. I'll give to you a cloak of green,
   To make you look like a fairy queen. . . .

7. I'll give to you the keys to my heart,
   Locked in love and never to part. . . .

9. I'll give to you the keys of my chest,
   And plenty of money at my request. . . .

11. Poor foolish girl, don't think it's so,
    It's only a joke from me, you know.
    Sure I wouldn't marry you, you, you,
    Sure I wouldn't marry you!

Woman.

2. I won't accept your paper of pins
   If that's the way your love begins.
   Sure I won't marry you, you, you,
   Sure I won't marry you.

4. I won't accept your suit of red,
   Stitched around with golden thread.
   (Sure I won't . . .)

6. I won't accept your cloak of green,
   To make me look like a fairy queen. . . .

8. I won't accept the keys of your heart,
   Locked in love and never to part. . . .

10. I will accept the keys of your chest
    With plenty of money at my request,
    And I will marry you, you, you,
    And I will marry you.

A PAPER OF PINS

Here is a love song with a funny twist, which I'm sure the boys will enjoy. This song lends itself to acting, so why not divide into "men" and "women" and see what you can do.

This version of the song was collected by Kenneth Peacock from Joshua Osborn of Seal Cove, White Bay, Newfoundland.

THE SAILOR'S ALPHABET

P.J. Thomas Collection

Adaptation and arrangement © by. P.J. Thomas

1. Oh, "A" is the anchor that holds a
   bold ship;
   "B" is the bowsprit that often does
   dip;
   "C" is the capstan on which we do
   wind,
   And "D" is the davits on which the
   jolly boat hangs.

Chorus
   Oh, hi derry, hay derry, ho derry
   down!
   Give sailors their grog, and there's
   nothing goes wrong.
   So merry, so merry, so merry are we;
   No matter who's laughing at sailors
   at sea.

2. "E" is the ensign, the red, white
   and blue;
   "F" is the fo'c'sle, holds the ship's
   crew;
   "G" is the gangway on which the
   mate takes his stand,
   And "H" is the hawser that seldom
   does strand.

3. "I" is the irons where the stuns'l
   boom sits;
   "J" is the jib-boom that often does
   dip;
   "K" is the keelsons of which you've
   heard told,
   And "L" are the lanyards that
   always will hold.

4. "M" is the main mast so stout and
   so strong;
   "N" is the needle that never points
   wrong;
   "O" are the orders of which we
   must be ware,
   And "P" are the pumps that cause
   sailors to swear.

5. "Q" is the quadrant, the sun for to
   take;
   "R" is the riggin' that always does
   shake;
   "S" is the starboard side of our
   bold ship,
   And "T" are the topmasts that often
   do split.

6. "U" is the ugliest old Captain of all;
   "V" is the vapour that comes with
   the squall;
   "W" is the windlass on which we do
   wind,
   And "X", "Y", and "Z", well I can't
   put in rhyme.

THE SAILOR'S ALPHABET

If you are fond of sailing or sea lore, you will enjoy this descriptive list of terms used by the crews of the old sailing ships. Besides helping the seamen to pull on ropes or haul up the anchor, such a song could spur new members of the crew into learning and understanding ship's jargon. It might be a good idea to make up your own alphabet when you want to remember certain things.

Most of the terms are self-explanatory. For the ones which may be new to you, here are a few definitions.

Capstan: *The anchor cable is wound around the capstan, and it took a team of men to push the capstan bars like a turnstile to make the capstan rotate. This work led to the singing of a fairly long and continuous song which was called a capstan shanty— or a capstan-and-windlass shanty if it accompanied pulling on the windlass.*

Davit: *Small boats such as lifeboats are slung from davits.*
Hawser: *a very thick, strong rope. In very early shipbuilding days it acted as a support for the hull of the ship in drydock.*
Stuns'l boom: *the boom of the studding sail, which is held by the irons.*
Jib boom: *a spar projecting forward from the bow.*
Keelsons: *Timbers bolted inside the hull to the keel to give the hull strength, especially where the keel curves most.*
Lanyards: *The stays and shrouds which support the masts are stretched by the lanyards.*
Quadrant: *a navigation instrument for determining position.*
Windlass: *the anchor winch.*

SIOUX LULLABY

Tah ne bah ne shan-ee-aze,
Ne shan-ee-aze,

Go to sleep my lit-tle one, my lit-tle ba-by
Fais do do mon beau pe-tit, mon pe-tit en-fant

ne shan-ee-aze Tah ne bah se, shan-ee-aze, shan-ee-
my lit-tle one. Go to sleep now, lit-tle one, lit-tle
mon beau pe-tit, Dors, dors, dors, dors, mon pe-tit, mon pe-

aze, Tah ne bah, Tah-ne bah.
one. Go to sleep, lit-tle one.
tit, Dors, dors, dors, mon pe-tit.

Tah ne bah, ne shan-ee-aze,
Ne shan-ee-aze, ne shan-ee-aze.
Tan ne bah se, shan-ee-aze,
  shan-ee-aze,
Tah ne bah, Tah ne bah.

Fais dodo, mon beau petit,
Mon petit enfant, mon beau petit.
Dors, dors, dors, dors, mon petit,
  mon petit.
Dors, dors, dors, mon petit.

Go to sleep, my little one,
My little baby, my little one.
Go to sleep now, little one, little one,
Go to sleep, little one.

SIOUX LULLABY

This lullaby was sung to me in Saskatchewan by an Indian friend called Dorothy Frances. Dorothy was a Sioux Indian, so we tried to write out the words in the Sioux language, and although this is what they sound like, I am not at all sure that we spelled them correctly. Anyway, Dorothy's version enables you to sing the words in Sioux as well as in English and French. To help keep the rhythm, which is not easy, try accompanying the song with a quiet drum beat.

SONG OF LOUIS RIEL

I send this let-ter to — you To tell my grief — and pain,— And
as I lie im — pri — soned I long to see — a - gain — You,
my be-lov-ed moth-er, And all my com-rades dear.— I
write these words in my heart's blood. No ink or pen — are here. —

2. My friends in arms and children,
   Please weep and pray for me;
   I fought to keep our country
   So that we might be free.
   When you receive this letter,
   Please weep for me and pray
   That I may die with bravery
   Upon that fearful day.

1. C'est au champ de bataille,
   J'ai fait crier mes douleurs,
   Où tout 'cun doute se passe
   Ça fait frémir les coeurs.
   Or je r' çois-t-une lettre
   De ma chère maman.
   J'avais ni plum' ni encre.
   Pour pouvoir lui écrire.

2. Or je pris mon canif,
   Je le trempai dans mon sang,
   Pour écrir'-t-une lettre
   A ma chère maman.
   Quand ell' r'çevra cett' lettre
   Toute écrit' de sang,
   Ses yeux baignant de larmes,
   Son coeur s'allant **mourant**.

3. S'y jette à genoux par terre
   En appelant ses enfants:
   Priez pour votr' p'tit frère
   Qui est au régiment.
   Mourir, c'est pour mourir,
   Chacun meurt à son tour;
   J'aim' mieux mourir en brave,
   Faut tous mourir un jour.

SONG OF LOUIS RIEL

Louis Riel was thought to have written this song, and since we know that he made up verses and poems all his life, it is possible that he composed these verses (or ones like them) when he was in prison, and handed them on to his friends. His story, which is also the story of the Prairie Métis, is a fascinating one, and I hope that this song increases the singers' interest in it.

After their defeat in battle, many of the Manitoba Métis settled in Lebret, Saskatchewan, where I collected this song. It was sung to me by Joseph Gaspard Jeannotte, one of the Métis living there, and before he started it he expressed his admiration for "their hero" Louis Riel.

SONG OF THE RABBIT

Uk - a lig - ei pis - ik - si - ni, Qi - lu laak - pauk
Lit - tle rab - bit, lit - tle rab - bit has a bow and ar - row,

san - u laak - pauk ig - i mai yai yai
has a bow and ar - row. He will shoot the ar - row.

ig - i mai yai.
a - ya ya ya.

Uk-a lig-ei pis-ik si-ni qi-lu laak-pauk
San-u laak-pauk ig-i mai yai yai,
Ig-i mai yai.

Little rabbit, little rabbit has a bow and
    arrow,
Has a bow and arrow.
He will shoot the arrow, a-ya ya ya.

SONG OF THE SEAGULL

Na - ja - na qut —— ni - ri - jut quu - qa - ni, sak ——
Sea - gulls are drift - ing, eat - ing and drift - ing, drift - ing. Fly - ing

wat - suk - lu - tit ni - ri jut, —— na - ja - na qut —— ni - ri jut. ——
fly - ing and drifting, eating, eat - ing. Sea - gulls are drifting, eat - ing, drifting.

Na-ja-na qut
Ni-ri-jut quu-qa ni,
Sak wat-suk-lu-tit niri-jut
Na-ja-na qut ni-ri-jut.

Seagulls are drifting, eating and
    drifting, drifting.
Flying, flying and drifting eating, eating,
Seagulls are drifting, eating, drifting.

SONG OF THE RABBIT
SONG OF THE SEAGULL

These two songs, which are much easier to sing than most Eskimo music, reflect the life and thinking of a people who speak of nature not as scientists but only as it is related to their way of life. They have developed a detailed knowledge of animals and birds because they must hunt to live, and they realize that in order to know what a bird or animal is going to do you must know what it thinks.

*Often animal behaviour is likened in Eskimo art to human thinking; for example, in **Song of the Rabbit** the "little rabbit" too is imagined hunting Eskimo style. Perhaps because seagulls are not valuable as food, they can be seen as just part of the landscape, "eating and drifting."*

Musically, as their collector Beverly Cavanagh points out, the songs have great variation in phrase length and a free rhythmic style. The final notes are very short, often followed by a hearty laugh.

*The translations are not literal, but convey the sense of the original. The Eskimo words have been included for both songs, and can be sung phonetically. **Song of the Seagull** suggests the rise and fall of the waves, and sounds very lovely played on a recorder or other simple woodwind instrument.*

WAY UP THE UCLETAW

P.J. Thomas Collection

Adaptation and arrangement © by P.J. Thomas

1. Come, all you bull-necked loggers,
And hear me sing my song,
For it is very short
And it will not keep you long.

Chorus
We had blankets for to travel,
Biscuits for to chaw.
We were in search of pitchbacks
Way up the Ucletaw.

2. We're leaving Vancouver
With sorrow, grief and woe,
Heading up the country
A hundred miles or so.

3. We hired fourteen loggers,
And we hired a man to saw.
We had a greenhorn cook,
And he run the hotcakes raw.

WAY UP THE UCLETAW

Here is a lumbermen's song made up in Vancouver about 1896, when there was a good deal of hardship among labourers, and a small tent town near False Creek was filled with unemployed hand loggers.

This song describes how loggers had to go up the treacherous winding part of the Seymour Narrows between Quadra and Sonora Islands known as the Yuc'ta (Yuculta) Rapids to find the pitchbacks: Douglas fir over six feet in diameter and over two hundred feet high.

*Heavy sap accumulated under the bark near the base of these giant trees, making it impossible to cut the bark. To get above this pitch layer or a flared butt (or if the ground was very uneven) the axemen had to fit spring boards into the bark. They then had a flat but not very safe base to stand on while they chopped. There are few—if any—of these trees left now, and in the day of the power saw it is hard to imagine how the men ever managed to fell them with their hand tools, working as they did under difficult and **dangerous** conditions.*

SONGS WITHOUT WORDS

Here are five songs which can be used for movement, to illustrate different time patterns or to express different moods. Three of them are very lively, and **She's Like The Swallow** and **Un Canadien errant** have beautiful, slow-moving melodies.

VIVE LA CANADIENNE

UN CANADIEN ERRANT

ZING, ZING, ZING

RATTLE ON THE STOVEPIPE

SHE'S LIKE THE SWALLOW